KINGDOM

CALL OF THE WILD

KINGDOM CREATED BY DAN ABNETT & RICHARD ELSON

CALL OF THE WILD

DAN ABNETT
Writer

RICHARD ELSON
Artist

Creative Director and CEO: Jason Kingsley
Chief Technical Officer: Chris Kingsley
2000 AD Editor in Chief: Matt Smith
Graphic Novels Editor: Keith Richardson
Graphic Design: Simon Parr & Luke Preece
Reprographics: Kathryn Symes
PR: Michael Molcher
Original Commissioning Editor: Matt Smith

Published by Rebellion, Riverside House, Osney Mead, Oxford, UK. OX2 0ES
www.rebellion.co.uk

ISBN: 978-1-907992-98-8
Printed in Malta by Gutenberg Press
Manufactured in the EU by LPPS Ltd., Wellingborough, NN8 3PJ, UK.
First published: March 2012
10 9 8 7 6 5 4 3 2 1

Printed on FSC Accredited Paper

A CIP catalogue record for this book is available from the British Library.

For information on other *2000 AD* graphic novels, or if you have any comments on this book, please email books@2000ADonline.com

To find out more about *2000 AD*, visit www.2000ADonline.com

DEDICATION

For Barrie Tomlinson. For giving me work when nobody else would and for all of your help and encouragement over the years. Thank you so much. – Richard Elson

For Ty. – Dan Abnett

CALL OF THE WILD

Script: Dan Abnett
Art: Richard Elson
Colours: Abigail Ryder (Progs 1657-1661)
Letters: Simon Bowland

Originally published in *2000 AD* Progs 1650-1661

BUT THAT WAS BARELY THE **START** OF THE SCRAPPING OF THAT DAY.

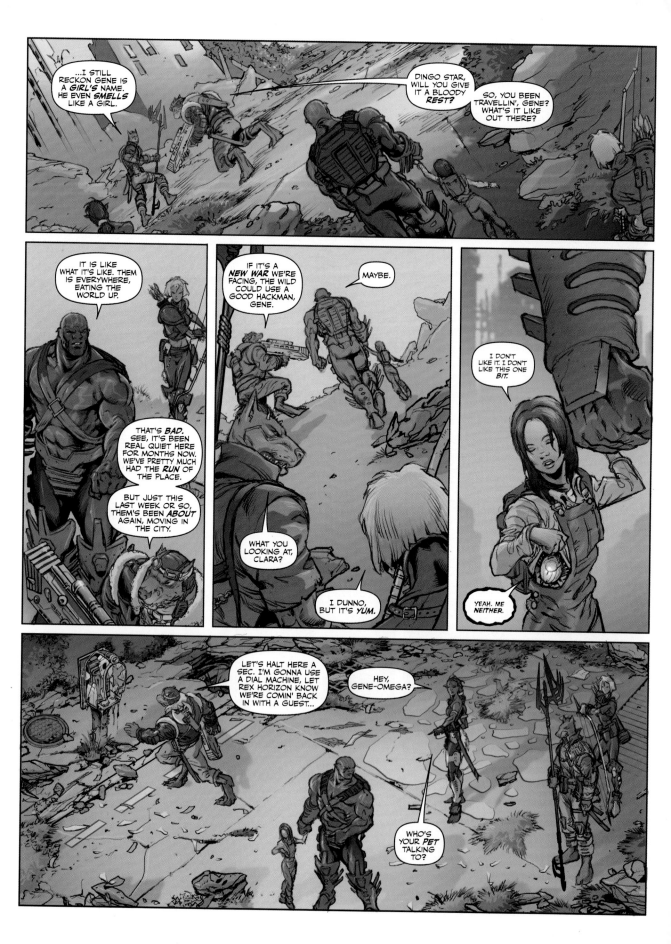

NO ONE *SENT* GENE.

BUT YOU'RE *FACTORY STOCK,* NOT *WILD-BRED* LIKE THESE ANIMALS.

WHAT'S YOUR BATCH NUMBER? YOUR UNIT *CALL-SIGN?* WHICH *BASE STATION* ARE YOU FROM?

WHICH COMCON AUTHORISES YOUR DEPLOYMENT?

YOUR MOUTH IS FULL OF STRANGE.

LISTEN TO ME! YOU'RE AUX. YOU'RE *CODED* TO TAKE ORDERS.

I NEED YOU TO LINK TO CENTRAL COMCON RIGHT *NOW* AND REPORT MY POSITION.

GENE DOES NOT KNOW HOW TO.

OF *COURSE* YOU DO! JUST FLIP DOWN THE SUBLIM RETINAL MENU AND SELECT GENERAL VOICE!

GENE DOES NOT KNOW WHAT THAT IS.

FOR CHRIST'S *SAKE!* THEY'VE GOT ME TRAPPED HERE LIKE A BLOODY *ZOO* ANIMAL!

LINK TO THE CENTRAL COMCON DATANET AND CALL IN AN *EXTRACTION!*

GENE HACKMAN CANNOT HELP YOU, PAUL NUMAN.

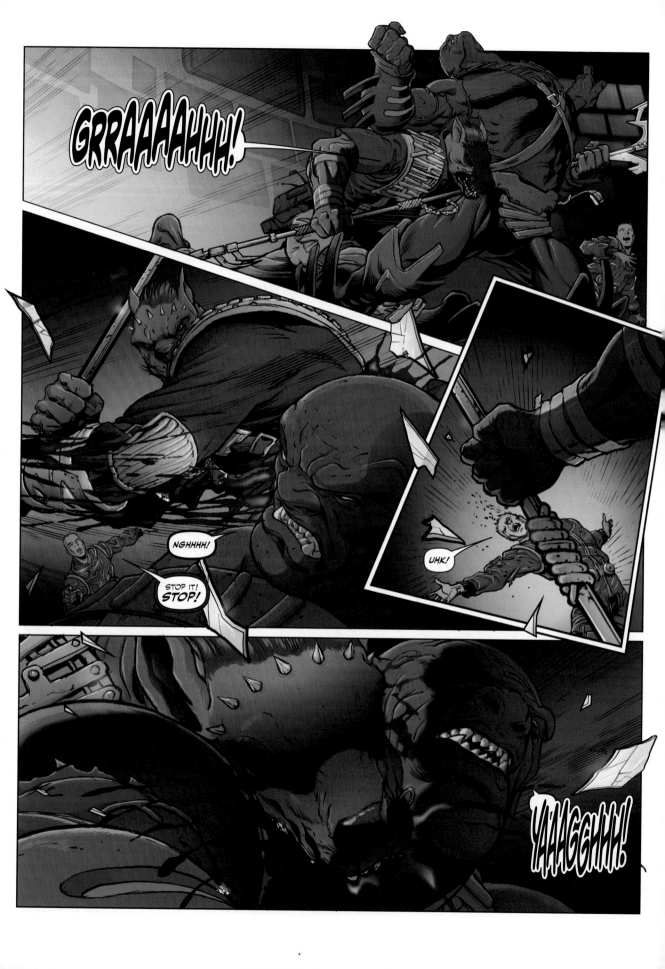

HIS MASTER'S VOICE

Script: Dan Abnett
Art: Richard Elson
Colours: Abigail Ryder
Letters: Simon Bowland

Originally published in *2000 AD* Progs 2011, 1715-1725

THIS IS THE TALE OF HOW HE DONE THE WALK-AROUND, AND HEARD HIS MASTER'S VOICE AGAIN.

ALL OF 'EM.

GENE HAD COME **WHISKER-CLOSE** TO A BIG BLACK RAK TWO DAYS BEFORE.

BIG MEAN THING. A **NEW** WAR FORM GENE HADN'T SCRAPPED WITH BEFORE.

IT HAD ALMOST LEFT GENE ALL BIT-UP AND KILLED DEAD.

GENE WAS **SURE** IT WAS THE BIG BLACK RAK WHAT WAS STALKING HIM.

AND THE BIG BLACK RAK, IT MOVED IN A WAY THAT WAS FULL OF WRONG.

IT GOT ROUND IN FRONT OF HIM SOMETIMES.

SOMETIMES HE GLIMPSED IT SHADOWING HIM, AND NOT WHERE HE **EXPECTED** IT TO BE.

AND IT GOT NO SCENT.

GENE OMEGA, HE KNEW THAT WHEN THE RAK FINALLY DECIDED TO MAKE ITS PLAY...

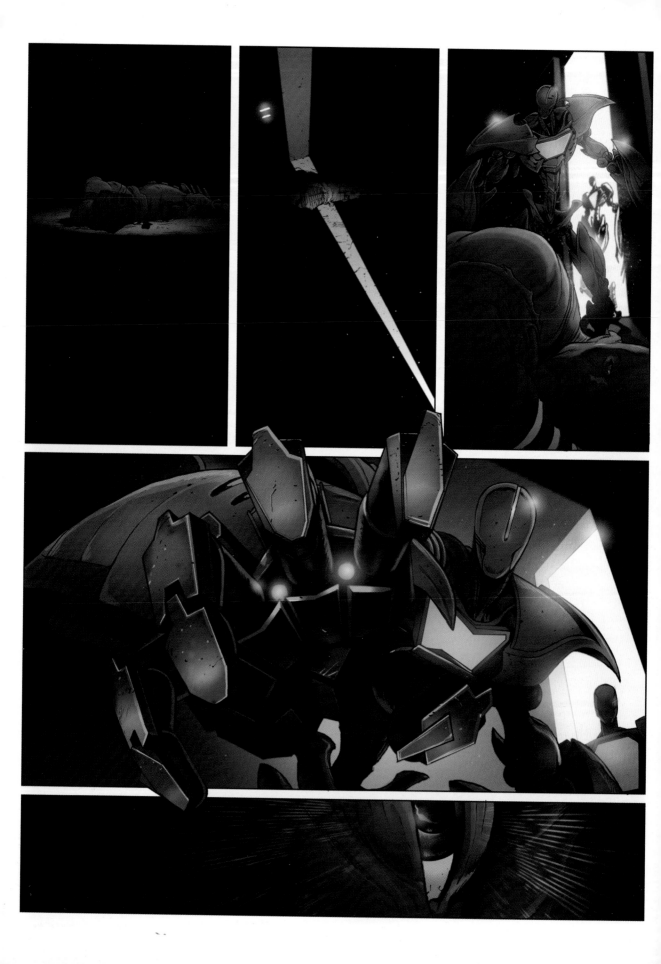

GET *OUT* OF GENE'S WAY--

...OR *GET WHET!*

THE POUND.

TROUBLE! I HEAR THAT TROUBLE AND *HOO-HAH* I TOLD YOU WAS COMING!

SOMETHING'S DEFINITELY *UP!*

I HEAR IT *TOO,* J.S. BARK!

YOU'RE RIGHT, BARK.

IT'S GENE THE BLOODY HACKMAN, *THAT'S* WHAT IT IS.

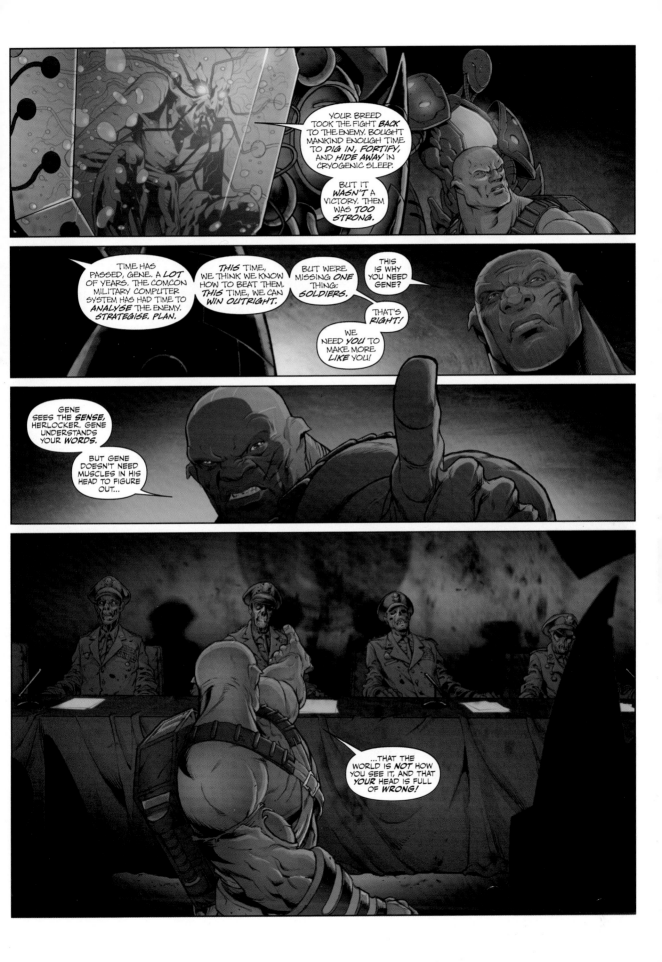

NEW MEXICO, SIX YEARS BEFORE THE BIG SLEEP.

USAF ACCOMMODATION COMPOUND.

HONEY? JOYCE?

DARLING! YOU'RE HOME SO EARLY!

I HOPE YOU CAN STRETCH DINNER TO AN EXTRA PERSON.

THIS IS JOHN.

JOHN?

HERLOCKER, MA'AM. IT'S A PLEASURE TO MEET YOU.

THE GENERAL'S SPOKEN OF YOU HIGHLY.

WE MADE A REAL BREAKTHROUGH TODAY, JOYCE. A REAL BREAKTHROUGH, AND IT WAS ALL DOWN TO JOHN.

I THOUGHT HE DESERVED A HOME-COOKED MEAL BY WAY OF A THANK YOU.

OF COURSE!

JACKIE WILL BE IN FROM LITTLE LEAGUE IN HALF AN HOUR.

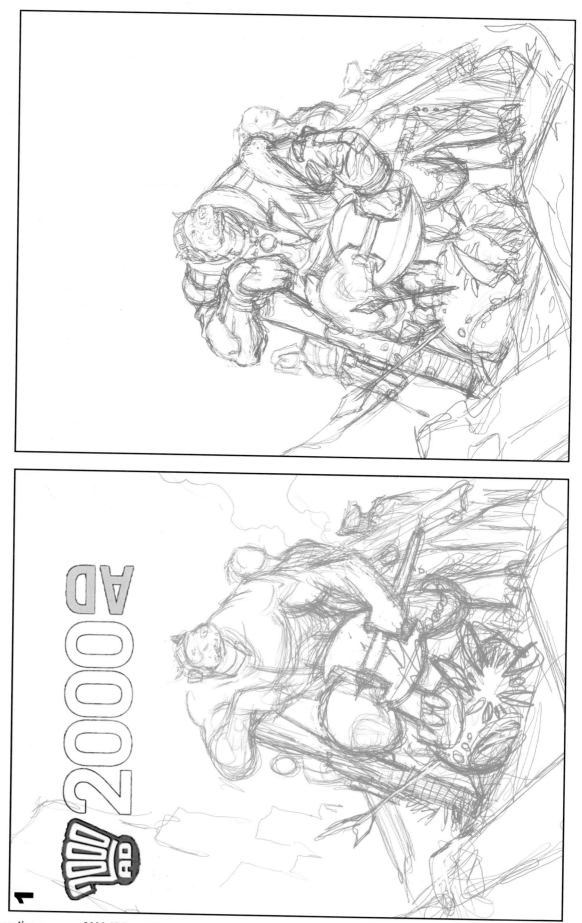

The creative process: *2000 AD* Prog 1652 cover from rough layout to pencils, inks and colour

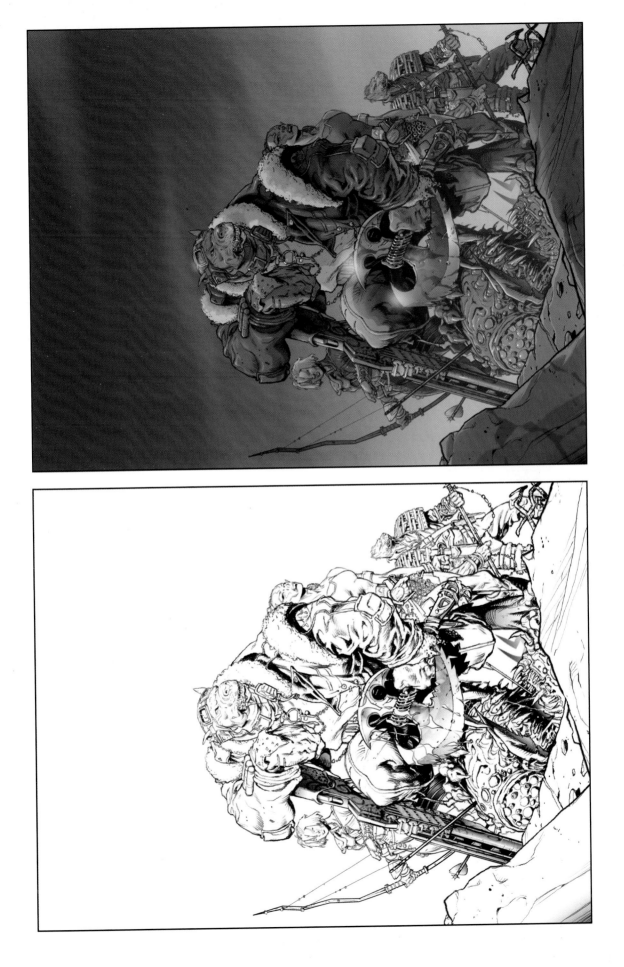

The creative process: Episode 1 page 6, from rough layout to inks and colour

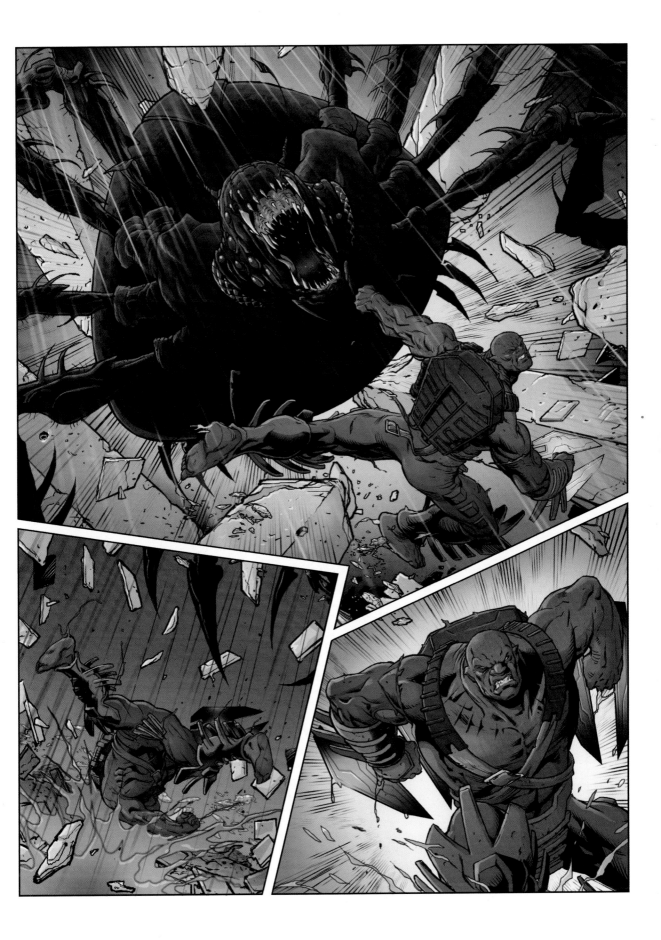

Brace on leg.

These small dogs always seem to have leg problems.

REX

Small, electronic devices.

Half chewed ear.

WILL

Rex to scale.

Pack character sketches

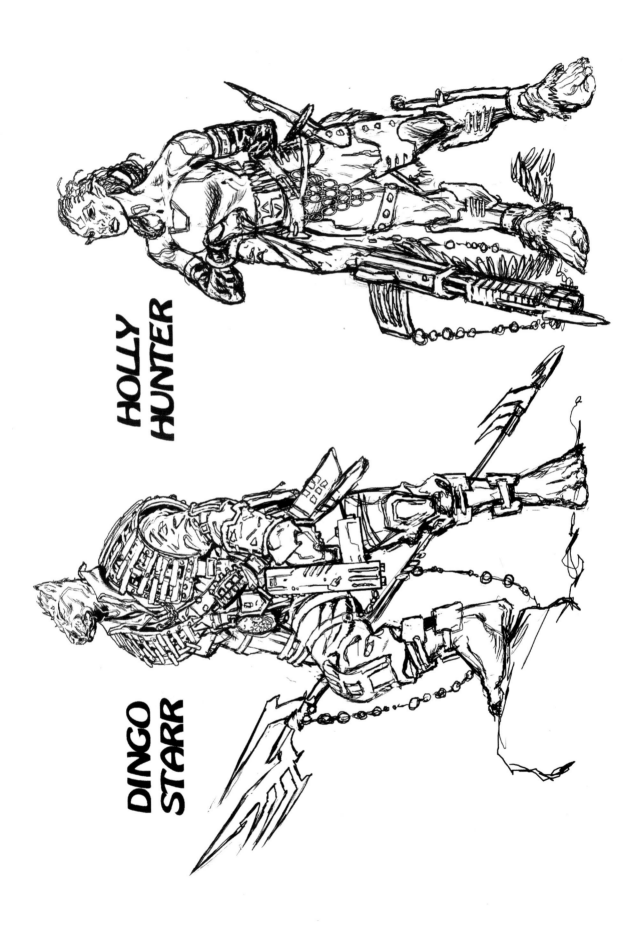

HOLLY HUNTER

DINGO STARR

CLARA
BOW

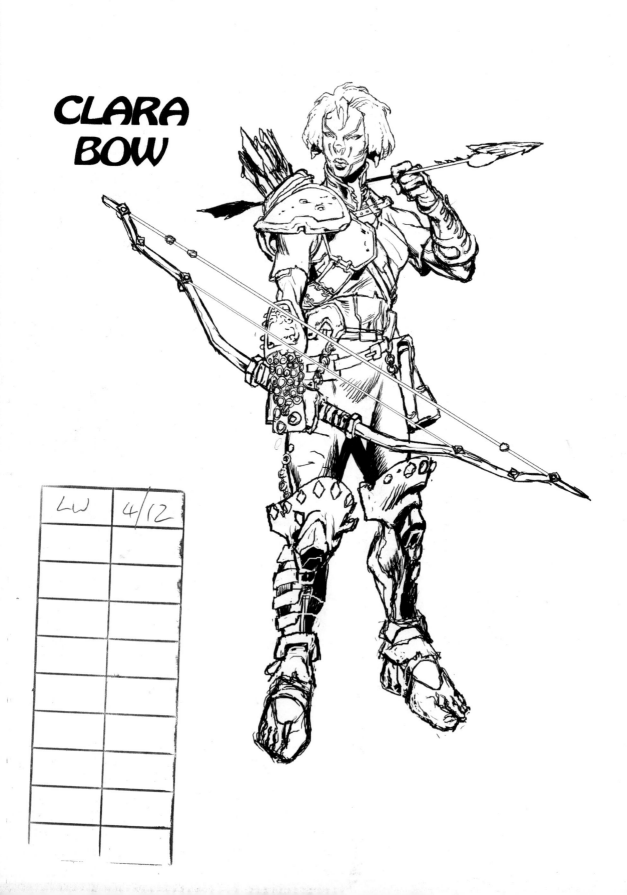

LW	4/12

DAN ABNETT

Dan Abnett is the co-creator of *2000 AD* series *Atavar, Badlands, Sancho Panzer* and *Sinister Dexter*. He has also written *Black Light, Downlode Tales, Durham Red, Flesh, Future Shocks, Judge Dredd, Pulp Sci-Fi, Roadkill, Rogue Trooper, The VCs, Vector 13* and *Venus Bluegenes*, as well as *The Scarlet Apocrypha* and *Wardog* for the *Megazine*. A prolific creator, Abnett has also written for Marvel, Dark Horse and DC Comics. He is the author of twenty novels for the Black Library, including the bestselling *Gaunt's Ghosts* series. His most recent work outside the Galaxy's Greatest Comic is DC's *Legion* and *Superman*, and Wildstorm's *Mr Majestic*. Dan Abnett was voted Best Writer at the 2003 National Comic Awards.

RICHARD ELSON

Richard Elson's first *2000 AD* work was on a *Future Shock* way back in 1988, and since then he has pencilled *Judge Dredd*, *Roadkill*, *Shadows*, *Time Twisters* and *Tyranny Rex*, as well as two co-created strips, *Atavar* and *The Scrap*. Richard has also illustrated several Marvel comics, including *Marvel Zombies Return: Hulk*, *Wolverine: Savage* and *Thor*.